C000203949

<u>Spelling is part of Primary English whether they like it or not</u>

<u>'Spelling Superstar or Spelling Swamp Dweller'</u> works by setting clear targets. We think kids do better if they know exactly what they're being asked to do...

> # <u>AT LEAST</u> 50% OF SPELLINGS MUST BE CORRECT
> # BY THE END OF THE YEAR

...and this book gives kids lots of <u>practice</u> to <u>make sure they do</u>.

<u>Here's how it works...</u>

1) Make sure the whole class knows that:
   - the point of this book is to BE A SPELLING SUPERSTAR
   - you stay a Superstar by <u>meeting targets</u>
   - to do well in primary English you must get <u>at least 50% of spellings right</u>

2) We've left a space for you to write a target at the top of each page, eg. 5/20 or 25%.

3) Targets should get <u>tougher</u> over the year.

4) If a child meets their target, they're a Superstar, but if they miss one they become a Swamp Dweller — until next time they meet their targets.

5) Then you can circle the Superstar or Swamp Dweller at the top of each page.

6) Even better, make a massive poster, with stickers for the kids' names. Move the names from Superstar to Swamp Dweller in a weekly ceremony. Give prizes for becoming a Superstar, and punishments for becoming a Swamp Dweller — may we suggest running round the school waving their hands in the air shouting, "I've got smelly pants and I don't care!" or doing the page again for homework.

Plurals of words ending in vowels

Copy out the words once, cover with the flap and write them again.

Get _____ right to become a Spelling Superstar.

Read	Copy	Cover
1) areas	1	1
2) radios	2	2
3) skis	3	3
4) sofas	4	4
5) zoos	5	5
6) bongos	6	6
7) kimonos	7	7
8) pianos	8	8
9) geckos	9	9
10) piazzas	10	10
11) patios	11	11
12) tattoos	12	12
13) cuckoos	13	13
14) cameras	14	14
15) casinos	15	15
16) sambas	16	16
17) umbrellas	17	17
18) kangaroos	18	18
19) armadillos	19	19
20) sombreros	20	20

EXTRA PRACTICE		
E1) haikus	E1	E1
E2) risottos	E2	E2
E3) tarantulas	E3	E3

Plurals of words ending in vowels

Put the flap over the last page and use the hints to work out the words.

Get _____ right to become a Spelling Superstar.

Hint hint	One last time...
1) Another word for 'places'.	1
2) Listen to FM stations on these.	2
3) Most important equipment for skiing.	3
4) Big comfy seats.	4
5) Places where wild animals are kept.	5
6) Drums played with your hands.	6
7) More than one Japanese robe.	7
8) Instruments with black and white keys.	8
9) More than one wall-climbing lizard.	9
10) More than one Italian market place.	10
11) Paved areas in back gardens.	11
12) Permanent ink designs on skin.	12
13) cucko _ _	13
14) Devices for taking photos.	14
15) Places in Las Vegas to lose your money.	15
16) Brazilian dances.	16
17) For keeping rain off your head.	17
18) Australian bouncing animals.	18
19) Animals that roll into hard balls.	19
20) Mexican hats.	20

EXTRA PRACTICE

E1) Short Japanese poems.	E1
E2) Italian rice dishes.	E2
E3) More than one big spider.	E3

Plurals of words ending in vowels

Copy out the words once, cover with the flap and write them again.

Get _____ right to become a Spelling Superstar.

Read	Copy	Cover
1) buffaloes	1	1
2) echoes	2	2
3) heroes	3	3
4) haloes	4	4
5) volcanoes	5	5
6) mangoes	6	6
7) cargoes	7	7
8) flamingoes	8	8
9) torpedoes	9	9
10) dominoes	10	10
11) larvae	11	11
12) macaroni	12	12
13) ravioli	13	13
14) criteria	14	14
15) spaghetti	15	15
16) strata	16	16
17) bacteria	17	17
18) fungi	18	18
19) tagliatelle	19	19
20) phenomena	20	20

EXTRA PRACTICE		
E1) vetoes	E1	E1
E2) tomatoes	E2	E2
E3) potatoes	E3	E3

Plurals of words ending in vowels

Put the flap over the last page and use the hints to work out the words.

Get _____ right to become a Spelling Superstar.

Hint hint	One last time...
1) Big hairy African cows.	1 ....
2) Hello... hello... hello... hello... hello...	2 ....
3) Spiderman and David Beckham.	3 ....
4) What angels have above their heads.	4 ....
5) Mountains that release lava.	5 ....
6) Sweet orangey-yellow fruits.	6 ....
7) The loads that lorries carry.	7 ....
8) More than one of these:	8 ....
9) Weapons that submarines fire.	9 ....
10) These things:	10 ....
11) Tiny baby insects.	11 ....
12) Pasta that goes well with cheese.	12 ....
13) Meat-filled pasta.	13 ....
14) More than one criterion.	14 ....
15) Long thin pasta (in Bolognese sauce).	15 ....
16) A posh word for layers.	16 ....
17) A posh word for germs.	17 ....
18) Lots of mushrooms or toadstools.	18 ....
19) Pasta in narrow strips.	19 ....
20) More than one unusual event.	20 ....

EXTRA PRACTICE	
E1) Turns down a proposal.	E1 ....
E2) Red fruits used in salads.	E2 ....
E3) Vegetable — can be roast or jacket.	E3 ....

Tricky plurals

Copy out the words once, cover with the flap and write them again.

Get _____ right to become a Spelling Superstar.

Read	Copy	Cover
1) houses	1	1
2) hisses	2	2
3) churches	3	3
4) foxes	4	4
5) fishes	5	5
6) balloons	6	6
7) patches	7	7
8) cities	8	8
9) tries	9	9
10) lorries	10	10
11) worries	11	11
12) puppies	12	12
13) jellies	13	13
14) buses	14	14
15) lunches	15	15
16) watches	16	16
17) meals	17	17
18) days	18	18
19) cries	19	19
20) parties	20	20

EXTRA PRACTICE		
E1) groceries	E1	E1
E2) bakeries	E2	E2
E3) footballs	E3	E3

Tricky plurals

Put the flap over the last page and use the hints to work out the words.

Get _____ right to become a Spelling Superstar.

Hint hint	One last time...
1) Buildings people live in.	1 ....
2) More than one snake noise.	2 ....
3) Buildings to pray in.	3 ....
4) More than one of these:	4 ....
5) They swim in seas and rivers.	5 ....
6) Inflatable fun at parties.	6 ....
7) Cover up holes in clothes with them.	7 ....
8) Bigger than towns.	8 ....
9) More than one try.	9 ....
10) Big trucks to carry large loads.	10 ....
11) Things you're concerned about.	11 ....
12) Baby dogs.	12 ....
13) Wibbly wobbly desserts.	13 ....
14) More than one of these:	14 ....
15) More than one meal at midday.	15 ....
16) More than one of these:	16 ....
17) Breakfast, lunch, dinner, supper.	17 ....
18) There are seven in a week.	18 ....
19) More than one cry.	19 ....
20) Invite your friends and open presents.	20 ....

EXTRA PRACTICE

E1) What you buy at the grocer's.	E1 ....
E2) Shops that sell bread.	E2 ....
E3) More than one of these:	E3 ....

More tricky plurals

Copy out the words once, cover with the flap and write them again.

Get _____ right to become a Spelling Superstar.

Read	Copy	Cover
1) calves	1	1
2) halves	2	2
3) wolves	3	3
4) knives	4	4
5) loaves	5	5
6) lives	6	6
7) scarves	7	7
8) selves	8	8
9) geese	9	9
10) mice	10	10
11) dice	11	11
12) teeth	12	12
13) wives	13	13
14) thieves	14	14
15) leaves	15	15
16) shelves	16	16
17) elves	17	17
18) women	18	18
19) lice	19	19
20) children	20	20

EXTRA PRACTICE		
E1) antennae	E1	E1
E2) formulae	E2	E2
E3) roofs	E3	E3

More tricky plurals

Put the flap over the last page and use the hints to work out the words.

Get _____ right to become a Spelling Superstar.

Hint hint	One last time...
1) Baby cows.	1 ....
2) More than one half.	2 ....
3) More than one of these:	3 ....
4) Cutting blades.	4 ....
5) The shape that you buy bread in.	5 ....
6) More than one life.	6 ....
7) Things to keep necks warm.	7 ....
8) sel _ _ s	8 ....
9) More than one of these:	9 ....
10) They get chased by cats.	10 ....
11) Roll them when you play board games.	11 ....
12) Use them for biting things.	12 ....
13) Married women.	13 ....
14) People who steal things.	14 ....
15) Green things that grow on trees.	15 ....
16) Put books or ornaments on them.	16 ....
17) Little pixies with big ears.	17 ....
18) Men and wo _ _ _.	18 ....
19) Posh word for nits.	19 ....
20) Young people.	20 ....

EXTRA PRACTICE

E1) On the heads of insects.	E1 ....
E2) More than one formula.	E2 ....
E3) They keep the rain off houses.	E3 ....

Word roots

Copy out the words once, cover with the flap and write them again.

Get _____ right to become a Spelling Superstar.

Read	Copy	Cover
1) assist	1	1
2) assistance	2	2
3) pain	3	3
4) painstaking	4	4
5) electric	5	5
6) electricity	6	6
7) hero	7	7
8) heroism	8	8
9) bore	9	9
10) boredom	10	10
11) govern	11	11
12) governor	12	12
13) prove	13	13
14) approval	14	14
15) relate	15	15
16) relative	16	16
17) prison	17	17
18) imprisoned	18	18
19) obey	19	19
20) disobey	20	20

EXTRA PRACTICE		
E1) sun	E1	E1
E2) sunburn	E2	E2
E3) sunbeam	E3	E3

Word roots

Put the flap over the last page and use the hints to work out the words.

Get _____ right to become a Spelling Superstar.

Hint hint	One last time...
1) Help someone out.	1 ....
2) Give someone as _ _ st _ _ _ e.	2 ....
3) Ow! I'm in _ _ _ _ !	3 ....
4) Careful attention to detail.	4 ....
5) ele _ t _ i _	5 ....
6) What your TV and lights run on.	6 ....
7) Super sort of person.	7 ....
8) Bravery.	8 ....
9) Make bored.	9 ....
10) Being bored.	10 ....
11) Rule.	11 ....
12) Ruler.	12 ....
13) Show something is right.	13 ....
14) Saying something is right.	14 ....
15) Connect two things.	15 ....
16) Someone in your family.	16 ....
17) Building for locking up prisoners.	17 ....
18) To be locked up.	18 ....
19) Do what you're told.	19 ....
20) Don't do what you're told.	20 ....

EXTRA PRACTICE

E1) Big orange thing in sky.	E1 ....
E2) Red, peeling skin.	E2 ....
E3) Ray of sunlight.	E3 ....

Word roots

Copy out the words once, cover with the flap and write them again.

Get _____ right to become a Spelling Superstar.

Read	Copy	Cover
1) act	1	1
2) actor	2	2
3) claim	3	3
4) exclaim	4	4
5) light	5	5
6) lightning	6	6
7) medic	7	7
8) medication	8	8
9) cover	9	9
10) discover	10	10
11) hand	11	11
12) handicraft	12	12
13) public	13	13
14) publication	14	14
15) shake	15	15
16) shakily	16	16
17) give	17	17
18) forgiveness	18	18
19) child	19	19
20) childlike	20	20

EXTRA PRACTICE

E1) fool	E1	E1
E2) foolproof	E2	E2
E3) foolish	E3	E3

© CGP 200

Word roots

Put the flap over the last page and use the hints to work out the words.
Get _____ right to become a Spelling Superstar.

Hint hint	One last time...
1) Pretend to be a character.	1 ....
2) Someone who acts.	2 ....
3) Say something's true.	3 ....
4) Yell out loud.	4 ....
5) The opposite of dark.	5 ....
6) A flash of light in the sky.	6 ....
7) Doctor.	7 ....
8) Medicine.	8 ....
9) Put a sheet over something.	9 ....
10) Find.	10 ....
11) On the end of your arm.	11 ....
12) h _ n _ i _ r _ ft.	12 ....
13) The general population.	13 ....
14) Writing that's been published.	14 ....
15) Wiggle up and down.	15 ....
16) She held my hand s _ ak _ l _.	16 ....
17) To pass something on.	17 ....
18) Stopping being angry at someone.	18 ....
19) A kid.	19 ....
20) Like a kid.	20 ....

EXTRA PRACTICE

E1) Silly person.	E1 ....
E2) Even a fool could do it.	E2 ....
E3) Very silly.	E3 ....

ci, ce and cy

Copy out the words once, cover with the flap and write them again.

Get _____ right to become a Spelling Superstar.

Read	Copy	Cover
1) cinema	1	1
2) city	2	2
3) circuit	3	3
4) citizen	4	4
5) decisive	5	5
6) recital	6	6
7) incident	7	7
8) century	8	8
9) cellophane	9	9
10) celsius	10	10
11) discern	11	11
12) except	12	12
13) cereal	13	13
14) cyanide	14	14
15) cynic	15	15
16) cypress	16	16
17) mercy	17	17
18) cylinder	18	18
19) fancy	19	19
20) cyclone	20	20
EXTRA PRACTICE		
E1) cistern	E1	E1
E2) certificate	E2	E2
E3) cemetery	E3	E3

© CGP 200.

ci, ce and cy

Put the flap over the last page and use the hints to work out the words.
Get _____ right to become a Spelling Superstar.

Hint hint	One last time...
1) 🎬 Place that shows films.	1 ....
2) Big town with a cathedral.	2 ....
3) Closed loop.	3 ....
4) Member of a state.	4 ....
5) Able to make a choice quickly.	5 ....
6) Reading out.	6 ....
7) Thing that has happened.	7 ....
8) One hundred years.	8 ....
9) Clear plastic film.	9 ....
10) Temperature scale. 🌡	10 ....
11) Recognise clearly.	11 ....
12) Not including.	12 ....
13) Breakfast c _ _ _ _ _.	13 ....
14) Poison. ☠	14 ....
15) Person with little faith in anything.	15 ....
16) A type of evergreen tree.	16 ....
17) Compassion.	17 ....
18) One of these: ⬮	18 ....
19) Individual taste.	19 ....
20) Whirlwind.	20 ....

EXTRA PRACTICE

E1) Water tank.	E1 ....
E2) Formal document.	E2 ....
E3) 🪦 Burial ground.	E3 ....

ie and ei words

Copy out the words once, cover with the flap and write them again.

Get _____ right to become a Spelling Superstar.

Read	Copy	Cover
1) chief	1	1
2) shield	2	2
3) fiery	3	3
4) review	4	4
5) obedient	5	5
6) ceiling	6	6
7) receive	7	7
8) receipt	8	8
9) deceit	9	9
10) conceit	10	10
11) vein	11	11
12) reign	12	12
13) weigh	13	13
14) neighbour	14	14
15) foreign	15	15
16) weird	16	16
17) their	17	17
18) neither	18	18
19) height	19	19
20) heir	20	20

EXTRA PRACTICE		
E1) protein	E1	E1
E2) perceive	E2	E2
E3) medieval	E3	E3

© CGP 20

ie and ei words

Put the flap over the last page and use the hints to work out the words.

Get _____ right to become a Spelling Superstar.

Hint hint	One last time...
1) Leader.	1
2) Protection.	2
3) Looking like fire.	3
4) Book r _ _ _ _ _.	4
5) Doing what you are told to.	5
6) Upper surface of a room.	6
7) Accept something.	7
8) Written proof of payment.	8
9) Lies.	9
10) Vanity, pride.	10
11) Blood vessel.	11
12) The time when a king or queen rules.	12
13) Measure something's weight.	13
14) Person living next door.	14
15) Not from this place.	15
16) Strange.	16
17) Belonging to them.	17
18) Not either.	18
19) Distance from the bottom to the top.	19
20) Person entitled to property.	20

EXTRA PRACTICE

E1) Essential part of the human diet.	E1
E2) Understand.	E2
E3) In the style of the Middle Ages.	E3

auto, bi, trans, tele and circum

Copy out the words once, cover with the flap and write them again.

Get _____ right to become a Spelling Superstar.

Read	Copy	Cover
1) autopsy	1	1
2) automaton	2	2
3) automobile	3	3
4) automatic	4	4
5) circumference	5	5
6) circus	6	6
7) circle	7	7
8) circulate	8	8
9) biceps	9	9
10) bisect	10	10
11) bilingual	11	11
12) biplane	12	12
13) telephone	13	13
14) telegraph	14	14
15) television	15	15
16) telepathy	16	16
17) transmit	17	17
18) transfer	18	18
19) transport	19	19
20) translate	20	20

EXTRA PRACTICE		
E1) autobiography	E1	E1
E2) transatlantic	E2	E2
E3) circumnavigate	E3	E3

auto, bi, trans, tele and circum

Put the flap over the last page and use the hints to work out the words.

Get _____ right to become a Spelling Superstar.

Hint hint	One last time...
1) Investigating a dead body.	1 ....
2) Robot.	2 ....
3) Car.	3 ....
4) Without instruction.	4 ....
5) Perimeter of a circle.	5 ....
6) Entertainment with clowns, tightrope...	6 ....
7) One of these: ◯	7 ....
8) Go round.	8 ....
9) Arm muscles.	9 ....
10) Cut in two.	10 ....
11) Knowing two languages.	11 ....
12) Aeroplane with two wings.	12 ....
13) Communication device.	13 ....
14) T _ _ _ g _ _ _ _ pole.	14 ....
15) Screen for recieving images.	15 ....
16) Reading thoughts.	16 ....
17) Send signals.	17 ....
18) Hand over ownership of something.	18 ....
19) Move from one place to another.	19 ....
20) Change into a different language.	20 ....

EXTRA PRACTICE

E1) Story of your own life.	E1 ....
E2) Across the Atlantic.	E2 ....
E3) Go round the outside of something.	E3 ....

in, im, ir, il, pro and sus

Copy out the words once, cover with the flap and write them again.

Get _____ right to become a Spelling Superstar.

Read	Copy	Cover
1) inactive	1	1
2) indecent	2	2
3) incapable	3	3
4) incredible	4	4
5) immature	5	5
6) impractical	6	6
7) impossible	7	7
8) improper	8	8
9) irregular	9	9
10) irrational	10	10
11) irresistible	11	11
12) illegal	12	12
13) illiterate	13	13
14) illegible	14	14
15) protect	15	15
16) project	16	16
17) propose	17	17
18) suspect	18	18
19) suspense	19	19
20) sustain	20	20

EXTRA PRACTICE		
E1) inaccurate	E1	E1
E2) irresponsible	E2	E2
E3) propeller	E3	E3

in, im, ir, il, pro and sus

Put the flap over the last page and use the hints to work out the words.

Get _____ right to become a Spelling Superstar.

Hint hint		One last time...
1)	Not moving.	1 ....
2)	Highly unsuitable, offensive.	2 ....
3)	Not capable.	3 ....
4)	Hard to believe.	4 ....
5)	Not grown up.	5 ....
6)	Not practical.	6 ....
7)	Not possible. *No Way!*	7 ....
8)	Not socially acceptable.	8 ....
9)	Uneven, not symmetrical.	9 ....
10)	Not rational.	10 ....
11)	Too strong to be resisted.	11 ....
12)	Against the law.	12 ....
13)	Someone not able to read.	13 ....
14)	Not clear enough to read.	14 ....
15)	Keep safe.	15 ....
16)	Long-term task.	16 ....
17)	Suggest as a plan.	17 ....
18)	Doubt someone's innocence.	18 ....
19)	Expectation.	19 ....
20)	Support.	20 ....

EXTRA PRACTICE

E1) Not accurate.	E1 ....
E2) Not acting responsibly.	E2 ....
E3) Revolving blades that propel a ship.	E3 ....

'shun' words

Copy out the words once, cover with the flap and write them again.

Get _____ right to become a Spelling Superstar.

Read	Copy	Cover
1) physician	1	1
2) magician	2	2
3) extension	3	3
4) collision	4	4
5) exclusion	5	5
6) profession	6	6
7) session	7	7
8) discussion	8	8
9) mission	9	9
10) passion	10	10
11) fiction	11	11
12) fraction	12	12
13) direction	13	13
14) diction	14	14
15) mansion	15	15
16) attention	16	16
17) ocean	17	17
18) Asian	18	18
19) Russian	19	19
20) Venetian	20	20

EXTRA PRACTICE		
E1) politician	E1	E1
E2) infusion	E2	E2
E3) proportion	E3	E3

'shun' words

Put the flap over the last page and use the hints to work out the words.

Get _____ right to become a Spelling Superstar.

Hint hint	One last time...
1) Doctor.	1
2) Someone who does magic.	2
3) Making something longer.	3
4) Crash, impact.	4
5) Leaving out	5
6) Someone's job.	6
7) A period of time set aside for an activity.	7
8) Conversation.	8
9) Task or goal.	9
10) Very strong emotion.	10
11) A story. Not real.	11
12) Not a whole number.	12
13) North, south, east or west.	13
14) Way of speaking.	14
15) Big house.	15
16) Care, applying your mind.	16
17) Large sea.	17
18) From Asia.	18
19) From Russia.	19
20) From Venice.	20

EXTRA PRACTICE

E1) Someone who takes part in politics.	E1
E2) The act of infusion.	E2
E3) Share.	E3

'shun' words

Copy out the words once, cover with the flap and write them again.

Get _____ right to become a Spelling Superstar.

Read	Copy	Cover
1) nation	1	1
2) station	2	2
3) intention	3	3
4) translation	4	4
5) education	5	5
6) demonstration	6	6
7) completion	7	7
8) deletion	8	8
9) repetition	9	9
10) position	10	10
11) petition	11	11
12) intuition	12	12
13) motion	13	13
14) lotion	14	14
15) devotion	15	15
16) promotion	16	16
17) distribution	17	17
18) pollution	18	18
19) revolution	19	19
20) institution	20	20

EXTRA PRACTICE		
E1) emotion	E1	E1
E2) contribution	E2	E2
E3) competition	E3	E3

'shun' words

Put the flap over the last page and use the hints to work out the words.

Get _____ right to become a Spelling Superstar.

Hint hint	One last time...
1) Country.	1 ....
2) Railway s _ _ _ _ _ _ .	2 ....
3) Aim or purpose.	3 ....
4) Changing from one language to another.	4 ....
5) Learning.	5 ....
6) Practical display.	6 ....
7) Finishing something.	7 ....
8) Rubbing out.	8 ....
9) Doing the same thing again.	9 ....
10) Where something is.	10 ....
11) Formal written request.	11 ....
12) Knowing something without knowing why.	12 ....
13) Movement.	13 ....
14) Cream that you rub on your skin.	14 ....
15) Great love.	15 ....
16) Advertising a product.	16 ....
17) Dealing out.	17 ....
18) Contamination.	18 ....
19) Uprising.	19 ....
20) e.g. University.	20 ....

EXTRA PRACTICE	
E1) Feeling, e.g. anger, love...	E1 ....
E2) Something given, e.g. money.	E2 ....
E3) Contest.	E3 ....

Words ending in ful

Copy out the words once, cover with the flap and write them again.

Get _____ right to become a Spelling Superstar.

Read	Copy	Cover
1) play	1	1
2) playful	2	2
3) care	3	3
4) careful	4	4
5) harm	5	5
6) harmful	6	6
7) wake	7	7
8) wakeful	8	8
9) scorn	9	9
10) scornful	10	10
11) beauty	11	11
12) beautiful	12	12
13) plenty	13	13
14) plentiful	14	14
15) mercy	15	15
16) merciful	16	16
17) bounty	17	17
18) bountiful	18	18
19) pity	19	19
20) pitiful	20	20

EXTRA PRACTICE		
E1) boastful	E1	E1
E2) doubtful	E2	E2
E3) colourful	E3	E3

Words ending in ful

Put the flap over the last page and use the hints to work out the words.

Get _____ right to become a Spelling Superstar.

Hint hint

1) Do this with a toy or game.
2) Fond of number 1).
3) Close attention.
4) Taking number 3).
5) Damage, hurt.
6) Something that harms.
7) Stop sleeping.
8) Feeling awake.
9) Contempt.
10) Full of number 9).
11) Quality of being really nice to look at.
12) Very very pretty.
13) Lots.
14) Being lots of — p _ _ _ _ _ _ _ _ .
15) Compassion.
16) Full of number 15).
17) Wads of money.
18) In great amounts.
19) Sadness for someone else.
20) Full of number 19).

One last time...

1 ....
2 ....
3 ....
4 ....
5 ....
6 ....
7 ....
8 ....
9 ....
10 ....
11 ....
12 ....
13 ....
14 ....
15 ....
16 ....
17 ....
18 ....
19 ....
20 ....

EXTRA PRACTICE

E1) Bragging a lot.
E2) Feeling doubt.
E3) Full of colour.

E1 ....
E2 ....
E3 ....

Lots of word endings

Copy out the words once, cover with the flap and write them again.

Get _____ right to become a Spelling Superstar.

Read	Copy	Cover
1) hidden	1	1
2) careful	2	2
3) sunnier	3	3
4) helper	4	4
5) burning	5	5
6) trainer	6	6
7) tricked	7	7
8) mopping	8	8
9) hummed	9	9
10) dropped	10	10
11) winner	11	11
12) write	12	12
13) runner	13	13
14) dream	14	14
15) disgusted	15	15
16) carrying	16	16
17) digger	17	17
18) rabbit	18	18
19) beeped	19	19
20) tricky	20	20

EXTRA PRACTICE		
E1) bother	E1	E1
E2) stopped	E2	E2
E3) feeler	E3	E3

Lots of word endings

Put the flap over the last page and use the hints to work out the words.

Get _____ right to become a Spelling Superstar.

Hint hint	One last time...
1) Hard to find.	1 ....
2) Taking care.	2 ....
3) It's s _ _ _ ier than yesterday.	3 ....
4) Someone who helps.	4 ....
5) Setting fire to things.	5 ....
6) One of these:	6 ....
7) I t _ _ c _ ed you by wearing a mask.	7 ....
8) Cleaning the floor.	8 ....
9) Hmmm mmmm hmmm.	9 ....
10) Not caught, but ...	10 ....
11) Not a loser.	11 ....
12) You should w _ _ t _ a letter.	12 ....
13) Someone who runs.	13 ....
14) Better than a nightmare.	14 ....
15) I'm shocked, in fact I'm di _ _ us _ ed.	15 ....
16) Picking up stuff and moving it.	16 ....
17) Machine that makes holes.	17 ....
18) What's this?	18 ....
19) That machine just b _ _ ped.	19 ....
20) A bit difficult to do.	20 ....

EXTRA PRACTICE

E1) Hassle.	E1 ....
E2) I st _ _ p _ d picking my nose.	E2 ....
E3) Someone who feels.	E3 ....

Lots of word endings

Copy out the words once, cover with the flap and write them again.
Get _____ right to become a Spelling Superstar.

Read	Copy	Cover
1) legality	1	1
2) simplify	2	2
3) possibility	3	3
4) kindness	4	4
5) foolish	5	5
6) criticise	6	6
7) medication	7	7
8) decision	8	8
9) collect	9	9
10) secrets	10	10
11) stressed	11	11
12) pressure	12	12
13) darken	13	13
14) mobilise	14	14
15) testify	15	15
16) correction	16	16
17) anticipate	17	17
18) expectation	18	18
19) necessity	19	19
20) intensify	20	20

EXTRA PRACTICE		
E1) reality	E1	E1
E2) nonsense	E2	E2
E3) ridiculous	E3	E3

Lots of word endings

Put the flap over the last page and use the hints to work out the words.

Get _____ right to become a Spelling Superstar.

Hint hint

1) l_g_ _ity

2) Make things easier.

3) A chance of it happening.

4) k _ _ d _ _ ss

5) Another word for silly.

6) Find fault with something.

7) Stuff to make you better.

8) Making a d _ _ isi _ n.

9) Gathering things up.

10) Things you don't tell anyone.

11) Under pressure.

12) Under pr _ _ _ u _ e.

13) Make it darker.

14) To start moving.

15) t _ _ t _ _ y

16) Making a wrong right. ✗ → ✓

17) Waiting for something to happen.

18) exp _ _ _ at _ _ n

19) Something that must be done.

20) in _ _ n _ _ fy

One last time...

1 ....
2 ....
3 ....
4 ....
5 ....
6 ....
7 ....
8 ....
9 ....
10 ....
11 ....
12 ....
13 ....
14 ....
15 ....
16 ....
17 ....
18 ....
19 ....
20 ....

EXTRA PRACTICE

E1) Not made up.

E2) Fewfvosihjbdvlalwibd. Eh?

E3) r_ _icu_ _ _ s

E1 ....
E2 ....
E3 ....

Dropping the letter e

Copy out the words once, cover with the flap and write them again.

Get _____ right to become a Spelling Superstar.

Read	Copy	Cover
1) living	1	1
2) caring	2	2
3) hoping	3	3
4) shaming	4	4
5) tuning	5	5
6) loving	6	6
7) waking	7	7
8) saving	8	8
9) using	9	9
10) timing	10	10
11) baking	11	11
12) miming	12	12
13) craving	13	13
14) shoving	14	14
15) coping	15	15
16) sharing	16	16
17) wearing	17	17
18) flaming	18	18
19) writing	19	19
20) taking	20	20

EXTRA PRACTICE		
E1) charging	E1	E1
E2) managing	E2	E2
E3) changing	E3	E3

Dropping the letter e

Put the flap over the last page and use the hints to work out the words.

Get _____ right to become a Spelling Superstar.

Hint hint	One last time...
1) Not dying.	1
2) Looking out for someone.	2
3) ☞ Wanting something to happen.	3
4) s _ _ m _ _ g	4
5) T _ _ ing the radio.	5
6) Really caring for something.	6
7) Getting out of bed.	7
8) Stopping something bad happening.	8
9) Taking advantage of something.	9
10) It's all about t _ m _ ng.	10
11) Making a cake.	11
12) Acting without talking.	12
13) Wanting something badly.	13
14) Pushing something hard.	14
15) Dealing with a problem.	15
16) Letting others use your stuff.	16
17) W _ _ r _ _ g clothes.	17
18) When wood's on fire, it's f _ _ _ _ _ _.	18
19) Wr _ t _ ng a book.	19
20) Opposite of giving.	20

EXTRA PRACTICE

E1) Running at someone fast.	E1
E2) Coping.	E2
E3) Swapping for something else.	E3

Changing y to ie

Copy out the words once, cover with the flap and write them again.

Get _____ right to become a Spelling Superstar.

Read	Copy	Cover
1) happiest	1	1
2) prettier	2	2
3) laziest	3	3
4) hungrier	4	4
5) windiest	5	5
6) fried	6	6
7) heavier	7	7
8) emptiest	8	8
9) supplied	9	9
10) tried	10	10
11) allied	11	11
12) varied	12	12
13) replied	13	13
14) married	14	14
15) carried	15	15
16) curviest	16	16
17) bouncier	17	17
18) craziest	18	18
19) cried	19	19
20) stickiest	20	20

EXTRA PRACTICE		
E1) rainiest	E1	E1
E2) friendliest	E2	E2
E3) spied	E3	E3

Changing y to ie

Put the flap over the last page and use the hints to work out the words.

Get _____ right to become a Spelling Superstar.

Hint hint

One last time...

1) The most happy.

2) Better looking than most.

3) The one who never does anything.

4) h _ _ g _ _ er

5) When the wind blew strongest.

6) I like _____ eggs.

7) Big Dave is he _ _ ier than me.

8) The thing with the least in.

9) Got everything they need.

10) Had a go.

11) a _ _ i _ d

12) Everything diffferent.

13) Response.

14) M _ rr _ _ d to someone.

15) Moved from one place to another.

16) The most curvy.

17) Bouncing more than most.

18) The most wacky.

19) Boo hoo.

20) The most sticky.

1 ....

2 ....

3 ....

4 ....

5 ....

6 ....

7 ....

8 ....

9 ....

10 ....

11 ....

12 ....

13 ....

14 ....

15 ....

16 ....

17 ....

18 ....

19 ....

20 ....

EXTRA PRACTICE

E1) The day with the most rain.

E2) The most friendly.

E3) Spotting something.

E1 ....

E2 ....

E3 ....

Different sounds spelt the same

Copy out the words once, cover with the flap and write them again.

Get _____ right to become a Spelling Superstar.

Read	Copy	Cover
1) right	1	1
2) weight	2	2
3) tight	3	3
4) freight	4	4
5) slight	5	5
6) height	6	6
7) pear	7	7
8) rear	8	8
9) search	9	9
10) year	10	10
11) heart	11	11
12) clear	12	12
13) fear	13	13
14) book	14	14
15) cook	15	15
16) hoot	16	16
17) loot	17	17
18) pool	18	18
19) root	19	19
20) took	20	20

EXTRA PRACTICE		
E1) fight	E1	E1
E2) hearth	E2	E2
E3) nook	E3	E3

Different sounds spelt the same

Put the flap over the last page and use the hints to work out the words.

Get _____ right to become a Spelling Superstar.

Hint hint	One last time...
1) Correct.	1 ....
2) Heaviness.	2 ....
3) Stretched.	3 ....
4) A f _ e _ g _ t ship.	4 ....
5) Only a small amount.	5 ....
6) How tall something is.	6 ....
7) Green fruit (not an apple).	7 ....
8) Back end.	8 ....
9) Look for.	9 ....
10) 365 days.	10 ....
11) Pumps blood round the body.	11 ....
12) The way was c _ e _ r.	12 ....
13) Feeling scared at danger.	13 ....
14) Rhymes with 'cook' and 'look'.	14 ....
15) Make a meal.	15 ....
16) Pressing a car horn.	16 ....
17) Stolen money.	17 ....
18) Swimming _ _ _ _.	18 ....
19) Underground bit of tree.	19 ....
20) I t _ _ _ four pieces of key lime pie.	20 ....

EXTRA PRACTICE	
E1) Punch-up.	E1 ....
E2) Fireplace.	E2 ....
E3) Little corner of room.	E3 ....

Different sounds spelt the same

Copy out the words once, cover with the flap and write them again.

Get _____ right to become a Spelling Superstar.

Read	Copy	Cover
1) bough	1	1
2) cough	2	2
3) enough	3	3
4) plough	4	4
5) though	5	5
6) bought	6	6
7) sought	7	7
8) thought	8	8
9) lie	9	9
10) tie	10	10
11) niece	11	11
12) piece	12	12
13) field	13	13
14) shield	14	14
15) grieve	15	15
16) armour	16	16
17) honour	17	17
18) rumour	18	18
19) pour	19	19
20) hour	20	20

EXTRA PRACTICE		
E1) brought	E1	E1
E2) thieves	E2	E2
E3) neighbour	E3	E3

  © CGP 200

Different sounds spelt the same

Put the flap over the last page and use the hints to work out the words.
Get _____ right to become a Spelling Superstar.

Hint hint

1) Branch of tree.
2) Clear your throat.
3) Plenty.
4) He needs to p _ _ _ _ _ the field.
5) On the other hand.
6) To have purchased something.
7) To have looked for something.
8) Past tense of think.
9) Tell the truth or tell a _ _ _.
10) Smart, useless bit of men's clothing.
11) Your sister or brother's child.
12) A little bit of something.
13) Area for growing crops.
14) The chieftain's s _ _ _ _ _.
15) Mourn a sad thing.
16) Protection for soldiers in battle.
17) Feeling of dignity and pride.
18) Gossip that might be untrue.
19) Let me _ _ _ _ you a drink.
20) 60 minutes.

One last time...

1
2
3
4
5
6
7
8
9
10
11
12
13
14
15
16
17
18
19
20

EXTRA PRACTICE

E1) Past tense of 'bring'.
E2) Robbers.
E3) Person who lives next door.

E1
E2
E3

CGP 2002

Spelling Book 3 — Tough Words

Homophones are words that sound the same, but have different meanings.

Homophones

Copy out the words once, cover with the flap and write them again.

Get _____ right to become a Spelling Superstar.

Read	Copy	Cover
1) cell	1	1
2) sell	2	2
3) beach	3	3
4) beech	4	4
5) him	5	5
6) hymn	6	6
7) knot	7	7
8) not	8	8
9) great	9	9
10) grate	10	10
11) by	11	11
12) buy	12	12
13) too	13	13
14) two	14	14
15) week	15	15
16) weak	16	16
17) stair	17	17
18) stare	18	18
19) tail	19	19
20) tale	20	20

EXTRA PRACTICE		
E1) their	E1	E1
E2) they're	E2	E2
E3) there	E3	E3

Homophones

Put the flap over the last page and use the hints to work out the words.

Get _____ right to become a Spelling Superstar.

Hint hint	One last time...
1) Room where a prisoner is kept.	1 ....
2) Give away in return for money.	2 ....
3) Nice sandy place next to sea.	3 ....
4) Kind of tree — sounds like 'beach'.	4 ....
5) Not her.	5 ....
6) Religious song.	6 ....
7) Tie in a bit of string.	7 ....
8) I am n _ _ going there ever again.	8 ....
9) Absolutely brilliant.	9 ....
10) Often done to cheese.	10 ....
11) The chip shop is right _ _ the house.	11 ....
12) Pay money for an object.	12 ....
13) As well.	13 ....
14) One plus one.	14 ....
15) Seven days.	15 ....
16) Feeble.	16 ....
17) One step of a staircase.	17 ....
18) Look long and hard.	18 ....
19) The bit of a dog that wags.	19 ....
20) A fairy story.	20 ....

EXTRA PRACTICE

E1) Belonging to them.	E1 ....
E2) They are.	E2 ....
E3) Over that way.	E3 ....

Unstressed vowels

Copy out the words once, cover with the flap and write them again.

Get _____ right to become a Spelling Superstar.

Read		Copy	Cover
1)	animal	1	1
2)	carpet	2	2
3)	easily	3	3
4)	factory	4	4
5)	literacy	5	5
6)	lottery	6	6
7)	library	7	7
8)	flattery	8	8
9)	family	9	9
10)	formal	10	10
11)	predict	11	11
12)	offering	12	12
13)	interest	13	13
14)	prepare	14	14
15)	primary	15	15
16)	doctor	16	16
17)	original	17	17
18)	smuggler	18	18
19)	centre	19	19
20)	definite	20	20

EXTRA PRACTICE			
E1) hospital	E1	E1	
E2) general	E2	E2	
E3) miserable	E3	E3	

Unstressed vowels

Put the flap over the last page and use the hints to work out the words.

Get _____ right to become a Spelling Superstar.

Hint hint	One last time...
1) Beast.	1
2) Material covering the floor.	2
3) Without difficulty.	3
4) Car f _ c _ o _ y.	4
5) Ability to read and write.	5
6) Gambling on 49 numbers on balls.	6
7) Place where books are kept.	7
8) Saying nice things about someone.	8
9) Your relatives.	9
10) Opposite of informal.	10
11) Guess what will happen in the future.	11
12) He's o _ f _ r _ n _ a good deal.	12
13) Concern and curiousity.	13
14) Get ready.	14
15) The first or earliest.	15
16) Medical guy.	16
17) Opposite of unoriginal.	17
18) Someone who smuggles things.	18
19) The middle.	19
20) Absolutely certain.	20

EXTRA PRACTICE

E1) Place for treating ill people.	E1
E2) Common or widespread.	E2
E3) Really unhappy.	E3

Unstressed vowels

Copy out the words once, cover with the flap and write them again.

Get _____ right to become a Spelling Superstar.

Read	Copy	Cover
1) abandoned	1	1
2) description	2	2
3) disinterest	3	3
4) Wednesday	4	4
5) reference	5	5
6) prosperous	6	6
7) frightening	7	7
8) voluntary	8	8
9) conference	9	9
10) interested	10	10
11) stationary	11	11
12) deafening	12	12
13) jewellery	13	13
14) compromise	14	14
15) explanatory	15	15
16) memorable	16	16
17) marvellous	17	17
18) secretary	18	18
19) abominable	19	19
20) literature	20	20

EXTRA PRACTICE		
E1) boundary	E1	E1
E2) desperate	E2	E2
E3) stationery	E3	E3

Unstressed vowels

Put the flap over the last page and use the hints to work out the words.

Get _____ right to become a Spelling Superstar.

Hint hint

1) Left by yourself.

2) Piece of writing that describes.

3) Lack of interest.

4) Day after Tuesday.

5) I needed a r _ f _ r _ n _ e for the job.

6) Wealthy and successful.

7) Scary.

8) Done for free.

9) Big meeting.

10) Showing concern or curiosity.

11) Stopped in one place.

12) Horribly loud.

13) Bracelets, necklaces and earrings.

14) You should reach a c _ m _ r _ m _ s _ .

15) Gives an explanation.

16) Easy to remember.

17) Fantastic.

18) Does the paperwork in an office.

19) Another word for 'horrific'.

20) Books.

One last time...

1 ....

2 ....

3 ....

4 ....

5 ....

6 ....

7 ....

8 ....

9 ....

10 ....

11 ....

12 ....

13 ....

14 ....

15 ....

16 ....

17 ....

18 ....

19 ....

20 ....

EXTRA PRACTICE

E1) B _ u _ d _ ry line.

E2) At your wit's end.

E3) Writing materials.

E1 ....

E2 ....

E3 ....

Service charge not included

ISBN 978 1 84146 169 4

9 781841 461694

E5S21

www.cgpbooks.co.